Chromecast User Guide

by Tom Edwards and Jenna Edwards

CHROMECAST HDX USER GUIDE

NEWBIE TO EXPERT IN 1 HOUR!

BY TOM EDWARDS & JENNA EDWARDS

Other Books By Tom & Jenna Edwards

*250+ Best Kindle Fire HDX and HD Apps for the
New Kindle Fire Owner*

Kindle Fire HDX User Guide: Newbie to Expert in 2 Hours!

*All New 7" Kindle Fire HD User Guide –
Newbie to Expert in 2 Hours!*

Amazon Fire TV User Guide — Newbie to Expert in 1 Hour!

ABOUT THIS BOOK

This book is a consumer guide specifically concerned with the Google Chromecast HDMI Streaming Media Player – the new Google streaming device. The book aims to answer any questions you might have regarding your Chromecast device such as:

- What is the Google Chromecast?

- How does the Chromecast work?

- What does the Chromecast do?

- How to set up my Chromecast?

- How to use my Google Chromecast?

- What can I do with Chromecast? More than you would have thought!

- What can you stream with Chromecast?

- How to set up Kindle for Chromecast?

- What are Chromecast's capabilities?

This new Google streaming device may be tiny in size, but has huge capabilities. It is a genuine competitor for the likes of Roku, Apple TV, and the latest Amazon Fire TV. This book will also look closely at:

- Google Chromecast apps.

- Setting up your Chromecast dongle.

- Using Chromecast settings to get the best out of the device.

- The latest Chromecast tricks and tips.

- Chromecast troubleshooting.

- Plus much, much more....

Table of Contents

A REMINDER ABOUT UPDATES

Before we start, we just want to remind you about the FREE updates for this book. The Chromecast and indeed all media streaming services, like Apple TV, Roku and the brand new Amazon Fire TV, are still in their infancy. The landscape is changing all the time with new services, apps and media suppliers appearing daily.

Staying on top of new developments is our job and if you sign up to our free monthly newsletter we will keep you abreast of news, tip and tricks for all your streaming media equipment.

If you want to take advantage of this, sign up for the updates HERE…

 http://www.lyntons.com/chromecast-updates

Don't worry; we hate spam as much as you do so we will never share your details with anyone.

INTRODUCTION

Welcome and thank you for buying the **Chromecast User Guide – Newbie to Expert in 1 Hour!**, a comprehensive introduction to the exciting possibilities that the Google Chromecast HDMI Streaming Media Player has to offer and the perfect companion guide for those new to streaming media from their computers to an HDTV.

WHY YOU NEED THIS BOOK

When you buy a Google Chromecast you could be forgiven for thinking that its sole purpose is to stream films and music from well-known providers like Netflix, YouTube, HBO GO, Hulu Plus, Pandora. Indeed that alone would, for many users, justify the very low $35 Chromecast price tag, but we are here to tell you that this seemingly innocent pocket-sized device offers you way, way more than that.

The trouble is that none of the extra benefits of the Chromecast are discussed in the flimsy set up pamphlet that comes in the box. That's where we come in! We've taken everything we know, scoured the official online Google guides, then read a whole lot more and put it all together for you here. What you are reading now is a user guide for both beginners and the tech savvy. This book contains the basics you need to navigate easily around your device but also the more advanced tips and tricks that will have you using your Chromecast like a pro before you know it!

HOW TO USE THIS BOOK

Feel free to dip in and out of different chapters, but we would suggest reading the whole book from start to finish to get a clear overview of all the information contained. We have purposely kept this book short, sweet and to the point so that you can consume it in an hour and get straight on with enjoying your Chromecast.

We will be updating this book on a regular basis and love getting your feedback, so if there is a feature that you find confusing or something else that you feel we've missed then please let us know by emailing us at bestkindleapps@gmail.com. Thank you!

So without further ado let's begin.....

1. WHAT IS THE GOOGLE CHROMECAST AND WHY SHOULD YOU GET ONE?

MEET THE CHROMECAST!

If you love great entertainment, you might have spent the past few years or so wondering when someone would develop a technology that would seamlessly combine the Internet with big-screen TV.

The two have always seemed to be made for each other, but like Romeo and Juliet, the stars never quite aligned to bring them together in happily-ever-after fashion.

All that changed in summer 2013 when Google released the Chromecast, a dongle that plugs into the HDMI port on your HDTV.

After going through a one-time setup process, the Chromecast will play your favorite movie, Internet video, music, or photo collection on your HD entertainment system.

The process begins on your mobile phone, tablet, Windows PC, or Mac.

Using an app on your phone or tablet, or your Chrome web browser on a PC or Mac, you can start playing your movie, song, or slideshow, and click a single command to begin "casting" (short for broadcasting) to have it appear on your HDTV.

The Chromecast finds your personal Wi-Fi network, picks up whatever is showing on the screen of your device, and mirrors it on your HDTV. It's stunningly simple!

WHY YOU'RE GOING TO LOVE THE CHROMECAST!

There are lots of reasons to fall in love with the Chromecast....

Instead of huddling around your computer to watch the latest movie release, you'll be sitting comfortably in your recliner with your favorite beverage and viewing it on your large-screen TV in high-definition quality.

Even better, the soundtrack is 'cast' to your HDTV right along with the video image, so there's no annoying separation of the audio from the video. You don't have to put up with the tinny little speakers on your laptop either – if you have a high-quality speaker system for your HDTV, the sound is going to be stunning.

The Chromecast mirrors your Internet media wirelessly, too, so you don't have to fiddle around with hooking up an HDMI cable to your computer or worry about tripping over it when you get out of your chair. And you'll never lose the remote, because there isn't one – all remote control functions are adjusted from your mobile phone, tablet, Windows PC, or Mac.

Finally, you're going to love the price tag. Sure, there are other devices that do many of the same things the Chromecast does, but not at the Chromecast's price of $35 (as of spring 2014). That puts HD Internet casting within reach of just about everybody, and there's no need to go out and buy any new equipment or cables before you can get up and running.

The only additional cost would be a subscription to your favorite online movie or music streaming service, if that's what you prefer. Just keep in mind that the Chromecast isn't proud – it also plays free videos like the ones you find on YouTube, and they look great in HD!

A NATURAL HISTORY OF THE CHROMECAST

It would be off-topic for this book to give a detailed history of the development of the Chromecast, and most of the really juicy details are known only to the folks at Google.

When Google released the device on July 24, 2013, the company would only say that the technology is based on its Chrome operating system for the web. However, the majority of the tech world agrees that the Chromecast is primarily Android-based.

If you own an Android smartphone or tablet, you'll be pleased to find a large number of Android-supported apps for the Chromecast. The iPhone has a lesser but still useful number of Chromecast apps, while Windows and Mac computers primarily rely on casting from Google's chrome browser.

We also know that Google has aggressively encouraged on-demand media companies like Netflix and HBO to quickly develop custom Chromecast-enabled apps for smartphones and tablets, along with optimized websites to accommodate Windows and Mac users.

Recently Google also released a software development kit (SDK) for the Chromecast to encourage independent developers to hurry up and build apps for it. These partnerships are mutually beneficial for both Google and the developers because it enlarges the customer base of both parties.

They're also a great deal for you, the Chromecast user, because that little dongle has big possibilities – and they're getting bigger all the time.

Finally, we have a strong hunch that the Chromecast will end up replacing Google TV, or more likely, merging with it. When Google

TV debuted in 2010, its popularity was dampened by the odd decision of CBS, ABC, and Hulu to block Google TV users from streaming their content.

The networks' decision would ultimately prove short-sighted, since Google wasn't blocking their ads on its TV service or changing their content in any way. However, it did slow down Google TV's momentum despite Google's huge captive audience of Android smartphone users.

With the Chromecast, Hulu has already gotten on board, so the future of the new device is looking good.

HOW IS IT DIFFERENT FROM APPLE TV OR ROKU?

With the Chromecast, Google decided to compete directly in the digital media player market, particularly with the bestselling Apple TV and Roku.

What makes the Chromecast different? The big one for most people is the price, with Chromecast coming in at about one-third of the price of an Apple TV or Roku box. Another selling point of the Chromecast stick is its size, which is slightly larger than your thumb and extremely lightweight.

Both Apple TV and Roku are set-top boxes measuring about 4" x 4". Roku has several different models in a range of prices and features. Both brand's devices are fairly heavy, and they're fragile enough to need a case for transport, so you can't just toss them in a purse or backpack as you can the Chromecast. Additionally, both Roku and Apple TV use an HDMI cable to connect directly to your HDTV, instead of a wireless signal like the Chromecast does.

Next, let's compare what these three popular digital media players can do for you, and their limitations...

Some people want to stream a tremendous variety of media to their HDTV – everything from first-run movies to pro basketball, hockey, and football, to arts and entertainment. If variety is your biggest priority, then Roku might be your best choice.

Roku offers its own library of 30,000+ movie titles, along with an amazing 1,200 proprietary Internet TV channels, most of them based on partnerships with major media companies.

A look at their channel line-up (www.roku.com) will remind you of the offerings on a high-end cable TV or satellite network service, only bigger and better. You'll see a basic selection of free news, sports, weather, entertainment, and radio, plus a long list of paid upgrades, such as Netflix, HBO Go, Disney, Walmart Vudu, and Amazon Instant Video.

And in an ironic twist, Google has partnered with Roku to offer a free YouTube channel for the first time on the Roku 3 device for 2014, even though the two companies sell competing digital media devices.

Apple TV also has its own proprietary channel network, and is fairly strong in the area of pro sports, but with only 30 channels, it can't compete with Roku. However, Apple TV has a couple of things that Roku doesn't have.

Apple's biggest asset is its enormous iTunes library, consisting of over 28 million songs, 45,000 movies, and 85,000 TV episodes. Apple claims this is the biggest media library in the world. Apple TV can also stream content directly from the Internet on your computer, which Roku can't do.

If you own a Mac computer, iPhone, or iPad, you'll find that they work perfectly with an Apple TV as long as you're running Apple's iTunes software. There's a Windows version of iTunes, but the pairing with Apple TV isn't always reliable, so if you use a Windows PC, or an Android tablet or phone, the Apple TV probably isn't your best choice.

The Chromecast's proprietary media network is the smallest of the three, with 16 providers available as of spring 2014, but more channels are being added all the time. Chromecast is unlikely to ever catch up with Roku, but it is sneaking up on Apple TV.

And while the Google Play store can't match the size of Apple's iTunes library, it's definitely well stocked with movies, TV episodes, and music, all of which are only available on the Chromecast.

Just like Apple TV, the Chromecast can cast web content from your computer, tablet, or smartphone to your HDTV. Unlike Apple TV, however, Chromecast doesn't lock you into iTunes software for web casting, so it works equally well on Windows, Android, and Apple operating systems, along with the Samsung Chromebook.

All three devices let you display "local" content – that is, media that you own and have stored on your computer's hard drive or on your phone or tablet. With Roku, you'll need to save your local content to a flash drive and plug it into the USB port located on the device.

Apple TV will cast any local content that's playable through iTunes, including movies, videos, music, and photos. The Chromecast also streams local content, but if it's not playable through the Chrome browser then you'll have to use the experimental "screencasting" function, which sends video to your HDTV but leaves the audio on the casting device speakers.

Most Chromecast users play their local content through a cloud-based server, such as Plex (more on this later), which lets you copy and store your local content on their enormous hard drives.

One final issue involves the image and audio quality on your HDTV. In this area, you really do get what you pay for. While most videos will look and sound great with Chromecast, occasionally you'll get one with poor resolution, or video and audio out of sync.

Since the Chromecast relies more heavily on the data processing power of your computer, tablet, or smartphone than Roku or Apple TV, the results you get from the dongle depend in large part on the capabilities of the device you're streaming from.

By now you've probably gathered that there are a few limitations to what the Chromecast can do.

However, there are also lots of workarounds. This book will show you how to get the same results with a Chromecast as you would get from Apple TV or Roku.

WHAT'S CURRENTLY SUPPORTED ON CHROMECAST?

There is already a huge variety of media available through the Chromecast, and you can expect more in the near future as more customers buy the device and everyone wants to jump on the bandwagon. Generally, these media services use the Chrome Internet browser to cast to your HDTV from your PC or Mac computer. If you're using a tablet or smartphone to do your casting, you'll need to download that media service's app first. Payment schemes for these vary – some are monthly subscriptions for unlimited content, while others are pay-as-you-go, and others are free.

Here's a brief summary of what you can get right now on Chromecast. This list is constantly being updated as more companies develop Chromecast-supported apps and content, so check back frequently for updates. (There's a rumor in the pipeline that Walmart's Vudu movie streaming service will join the party sometime in 2014, so look for it.)

Netflix: The biggest and best known of the Internet movie streaming services offers you movies, TV shows, and original Netflix programming. Payment is via a monthly subscription fee.

HBO Go: Features movies, TV shows, sports, comedy, and HBO original productions. An HBO subscription through your cable or dish provider is required, but HBO Go is a free add-on to your subscription.

Google Play Movies and TV: The search engine giant offers a great selection of movies and TV shows for rental or purchase on a per-item basis, instead of a monthly subscription plan like Netflix uses.

Hulu Plus: This upgrade to the Hulu service offers an amazing selection of TV programming. Payment is by monthly subscription plus a limited number of commercials to keep the price low.

YouTube: This Google-owned company is the largest source of free videos on the Internet, including movie clips, music, and independently produced original programming. Keep in mind that it's partially ad-supported, so you'll need to close some pop-ups from time to time.

Crackle: Like Netflix and HBO Go, Crackle offers movies, TV shows, and original programming. The company is owned by Sony Pictures Entertainment, so there's heavy emphasis on Sony-produced titles. Formerly known as Grouper, Crackle is free and has commercials.

Rdio: From the creators of Skype, this Internet music service lets you build your own playlists or choose from a line-up of radio stations. As well as free web streaming, Rdio offers Android and iPhone apps as well as a proprietary desktop app for Mac computers. Web streaming is free, with a paid upgrade to use it on mobile devices and eliminate advertising.

Vevo: The most visited music site on the Internet, featuring music videos from most of the major record labels. Vevo is ad-supported, so the content is free.

Viki: For an international viewing experience, check out this Asia-based movie, TV, and music channel, available in 160+ languages. Choose the free, ad-supported version, or you can upgrade to ad-free with a monthly VikiPass subscription.

Pandora: The original open source Internet radio project with channels in every musical genre. The free version is ad-supported, with an ad-free paid upgrade.

Songza: Internet music station with playlists curated by musical experts and tailored for your moods and activities. Free, ad-supported.

Google Play Music: A huge library of songs for streaming or downloading, including a number of free selections.

Red Bull TV: Enjoy feature-length movies, interviews, and breaking news for free on topics ranging from motocross to hockey to break dancing to extreme snowsports. Ad-supported.

Post TV: The Washington Post is the first newspaper in the US to climb aboard the Chromecast bandwagon, offering free news, features, sports, and interviews. Access is free.

Plex: This cloud-based media organizer stores all of your digital content in one place so you can access it from any device at any time. Basic features are free; expanded features are available with purchase of the premium Plex Pass (We cover Plex in more detail in **Chapter 4**).

RealPlayer Cloud: Completely private, cloud-based video sharing with your family and friends. 2GB of storage is included with a free account, with more space available via subscription upgrade.

Photowall for Chromecast: A Google-owned collaborative project that lets you share your photos for free through Google Play.

2. GETTING STARTED: THE BASICS

The "instruction manual" that comes with the Chromecast consists of a single page of instructions on the inside flap of the package. It gives three steps:

1. plug it in

2. switch input

3. set it up

While we agree with Google that the installation of this device is pretty simple, it's not quite that simple....

Remember you always need to be within range of a Wi-Fi network, since that's how your Chromecast receives a signal from your casting device.

Also, you'll need to keep your wireless network password on hand during the set-up process. Things are much simpler on the receiving end – any digital TV with an HDMI port will work.

Now follow these simple set-up steps… (Should you encounter any problems please refer to our trouble shooting section at the **end of this chapter**).

1. PLUG IT IN

The Chromecast has a male HDMI plug that fits into the female HDMI port on your HDTV. Sometimes this port is located on the back of the TV in a hard-to-reach spot or a tight notch. If this is the case with your TV, go ahead and add the optional HDMI extender that comes bundled with the Chromecast.

Plug the extender into the TV port, and plug the Chromecast dongle into the other end of the extender. This will make it easier to unplug the dongle without moving the TV, and if your TV is nestled close to a wall or inside a cabinet, it may improve the dongle's Wi-Fi reception.

Now unwrap the USB cable and adapter. The Chromecast needs power to operate, so your next step is to insert the micro end of the USB cable into the micro port on end of the dongle. To power it up, you have two choices. The recommended choice is to plug the other end of the USB cable into the power adapter and plug the adapter into a power strip or wall outlet.

However, we have had good results by simply plugging the USB cable into the USB port on our HDTV and using that to power the Chromecast. It's easier, and it leaves fewer stray power cords flopping around.

When the dongle is powered up but not plugged into the HDMI slot, the indicator light will be red. When it's connected to your TV and ready to cast, the light will change to bluish-white. The dongle will feel warm when it's connected.

2. SWITCH INPUT

Next, you need to change your TV's settings so it's getting its signal from the HDMI port where the dongle is plugged in, instead of from your cable service, DVD, or other signal. Many newer TV's will automatically detect a new input source. If this is the case, you'll immediately see the words "Set Me Up" on your TV screen.

If your TV doesn't auto-detect the Chromecast, then the easiest way to change your input is with your remote. Look for a button labelled Input or Source, press it to display the input device menu, and choose the HDMI slot that your Chromecast is plugged into.

You can also bring up the input device menu by pressing a button on the side or bottom edge of the TV itself. You'll know you've chosen the correct HDMI input when "Set Me Up" appears on your TV screen.

3. SET IT UP

Here's where you set up your casting device so it sends a wireless signal to the Chromecast plugged into your HDTV. You can cast from a Windows PC, a Mac desktop or laptop, a tablet (either Android or iPad), or a smartphone. Fortunately, you only need to go through the setup process once. After you finish, you can add more devices to cast without having to go through set-up all over again.

Setting up is a bit easier to do from a Windows or Mac computer, so we give those instructions first. If you don't have a computer, you'll find instructions for setting up from a tablet or smartphone a bit further along in this chapter.

Power up your PC or Mac. This step of the process gives the Chromecast access to your Wi-Fi network, so you'll want to make sure your computer is connected to the wireless network you'll be using. Have your network name and password handy.

The "Set Me Up" display on your TV will show a website address: http://www.google.com/chromecast/setup

You'll need to use the Chrome browser on your computer to navigate to this address. If you don't have Chrome yet, go ahead and use your current web browser to download and install it from http://www.google.com/chrome/

On the set-up page, you should see the message, "Welcome, let's get you set up and casting," with a blue Download button below it. Click the blue button and follow the prompts to install the Chromecast app on your machine.

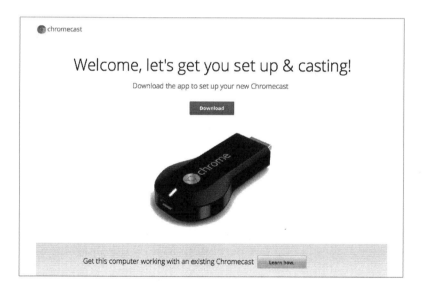

After downloading, the app should start automatically. If it doesn't, then you can double-click its icon on your desktop, or navigate to your Downloads folder and open it from there.

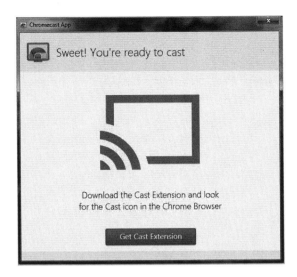

The app will detect your wireless network automatically and assign it a random number, such as **Chromecast1234**. It also assigns a temporary code for set-up purposes only. Make sure the number on your computer screen matches the number on your TV screen and then click "That's My Code."

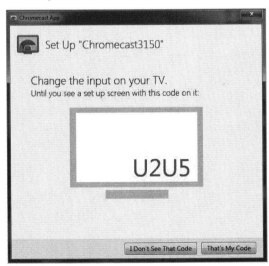

The Chromecast app should automatically detect your Wi-Fi network name, but if it doesn't, enter it at the prompt. Enter your password in the field provided. You can give your Chromecast its own name if you like – this can be handy if you're using more than one dongle in your house and need to tell them apart. Click *Continue*.

In the next screen, follow the prompts to download the Google Cast extension for the Chrome browser. The **Get Cast Extension** button will either download the extension directly, or it will take you to the **Chrome Web Store** (https://chrome.google.com/webstore/category/apps), where you'll click the + *Free* button to download and install. This extension allows you to cast directly from your browser as well as from the Chromecast app, which opens up even more sources of videos and music for you – in fact, it puts the entire Internet on your HDTV, but more on that later.

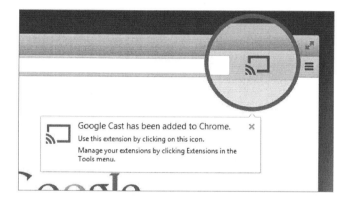

That's it – you're ready to cast! In fact, you should see a display on your TV screen telling you just that.

Smartphone and tablet users: If you don't have a computer and will only be casting from a tablet or smartphone, you can download the Chromecast app directly to your device. For Android devices, the app is in the Google Play app store. For iOS devices, the app is in iTunes.

Both versions of the app are free. Make sure you get the official version and not a knock-off by verifying that Google is the author of the app before you download it.

Follow the prompts during the installation process. Most of the commands will be similar to the steps above for installing the app on a computer, except you won't need the Google Cast browser extension. You'll know you've made the installation successfully when you see the "Ready to Cast" screen on your TV.

The **Kindle Fire** tablets from Amazon are, sadly, a different creature from your standard Android tablet and we discuss using the Chromecast with your Kindle Fire **later in the book**.

START CASTING

For your first cast, YouTube.com is a good place to start (unless you've already signed up for a paid video service and downloaded its app).

If you're casting from a PC or Mac, use the Chrome browser to navigate to YouTube. If casting from a tablet or smartphone, you'll need to download the YouTube app from the appropriate app store for your device and open it. Now open up a YouTube video that's labeled HD on the black toolbar that runs across the bottom edge of the video and let it launch. Also on the black toolbar, look for the Chromecast icon:

Click it to start casting the video on your HDTV. If there's no Chromecast icon in the black toolbar, look for it on the right side of the top toolbar of your Chrome browser menu. Click it and choose your Chromecast device name from the dropdown menu.

Tap the square icon in the lower right corner of the video to change over to full screen view. Now enjoy the amazing picture and sound quality on your HDTV. You can simply use the volume control on your device and the pause and play buttons in your app or browser window to control the picture and sound. Look, Ma – no remote!

OPTIMIZING VIDEO QUALITY

When HDTV was first developed, it took a while for the video quality to catch up with the hardware. That's less true today, but you still need to keep in mind that your casting is only as good as the quality of the video you've chosen.

YouTube, with so much free content available, has been especially slow in upgrading to HD, but they've been aggressive about promoting it to their publishers, so it's constantly improving. Still, the old Flash videos lingering on YouTube point up how far we've come in a very short time.

Another factor in the quality of your video display is your Wi-Fi network. If it's not as robust as it should be, then one of the tweaks you can make to improve it is lowering your settings. The Chromecast relies on a steady Wi-Fi connection to stream content.

If videos are choppy or suffering from constant buffering interruptions, your best bet is to reduce your video playback settings. Open your Chrome browser and access your Chromecast settings by clicking the small Chromecast icon (**shown above**) in the upper right corner.

Select Options from the drop-down menu and reduce your streaming to Standard (480p). Your videos won't be HD, but they'll still look OK, and you'll be rid of the constant buffering and interruptions.

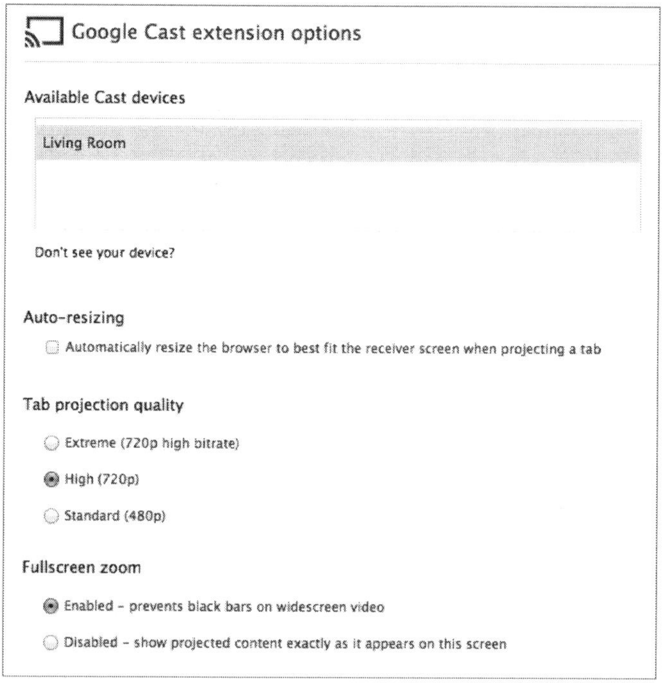

On a related topic, if you're running more than one Chromecast at a time in your home on separate TV sets, then it's going to drastically increase the bandwidth usage on your Internet connection. Although we've never had a warning from our Internet provider that we're using too much data, we've heard of it happening.

The more likely result, though, is that simultaneous casting to more than one device will slow down all of them. If you have a "lite" or "basic" subscription from your Internet provider, you might want to consider upgrading to a plan that gives you a bigger share of bandwidth.

SOLVING PROBLEMS WITH INSTALLATION OR CASTING

Most users will find setting up their Chromecast a breeze but if you run into problems it may be linked to your router or the operating system of the device you are casting from.

DO YOU HAVE AN OLD ROUTER?

If you're like most users, you probably don't pay much attention to your wireless router, which is usually a square box connected to your cable or DSL modem. Routers manufactured before approximately 2009 may be 5 GHz instead of 2.4 GHz, which is not compatible with the Chromecast. If you have one of these boxes, you'll have to replace it with a newer one.

The easiest way to find out is to get the model number of your router on the outside of the case and look it up on the Internet to find the specs. If you are not sure, Google maintains a list of popular routers and their specs on the web – you can check your router here – https://support.google.com/chromecast/table/3477832

YOU MUST BE WIRELESS!

Another thing to keep in mind is that you must use a wireless network for casting, so if your Windows or Mac computer is connected to the internet with an Ethernet cable, you'll need to buy and install a wireless router and switch over to a wireless connection.

If you see a cable plugged into the back of your computer that looks like an oversized telephone jack, then you're still wired and will need to go wireless. If you're a smartphone or tablet user, make sure your device is set to connect to the internet through Wi-Fi, instead of through a 4G connection from a cell phone tower.

SYSTEM REQUIREMENTS

Take a quick look at the operating system of the device you'll be casting from to make sure it's supported by Chromecast. If your laptop, tablet or phone doesn't meet these requirements, you will need to update your software or upgrade your device if you want to start casting....

Windows PC: Windows 7 or higher.

Mac OS desktop or laptop: OS 10.7 or higher

Android smartphone or tablet: Android 2.3 or higher

iPhone or iPad: iOS 6 or higher

Chromebook: Chrome OS 28 or higher

If the instructions in this book still don't result in a clean installation of your Chromecast, or if issues pop up after you've started using it, go to Google's troubleshooting pages – https://support.google.com/chromecast

If these don't solve your problem, feel free to call **Google's live telephone support** for the Chromecast. Select your country from the list provided. The US and Australia have 24/7 tech support. We have found their techs to be smart and helpful – a breath of fresh air!

3. WHAT ELSE CAN I WATCH?

At the end of **Chapter 1** we provided a list of Internet content providers like Netflix and Hulu that have already developed Chromecast-supported websites and apps. However, we think this topic needs a bit more explanation.

If you're using your tablet or smartphone to cast, then you already know what an app is – it's a specialized software program that helps your device perform one specific task. All of **Google's preferred Chromecast content providers** have developed apps for both Android and iOS for iPhone. As a reward for making their movies, music, and other copyright-protected content available to Chromecast users, Google has rewarded them with rockstar billing on Google's Chromecast website.

There are hundreds of other independent software developers creating Android and iOS apps for the Chromecast, but because these apps perform smaller tasks, Google hasn't rewarded them with rockstar status. Android users can find all these apps on their device by going to the app section of the Google Play store and searching for "Chromecast".

To cast from your tablet or smartphone, download the app for the media you want to cast. For example, to cast from Google Movies and TV, you will need to download the **Google Movies and TV app for Chromecast** from the Google Play store (Android) or from the iTunes store (iOS).

To cast a movie, purchase your title from the **Google Play store**, open it in the Google Movies and TV app, and click the Chromecast icon in the top toolbar.

Windows and Mac users may occasionally use apps on their computers as well. For example, Rdio, one of Google's preferred Chromecast content providers, has developed a Mac computer app to run its service so Mac users don't have to cast Rdio from a tab in Chrome.

However, very few other developers have developed desktop apps for the Chromecast, so virtually all casting from a computer will need to be done from within the Chrome browser.

Although Windows and Mac users don't get to enjoy dedicated apps like tablet and smartphone users do, a few of Google's preferred Chromecast content providers have optimized their sites for casting. Look for the Chromecast icon in a toolbar at either the top or bottom of the provider's website.

Currently there are four preferred providers who have optimized: Netflix, YouTube, Google Movies and TV, and Google Play Music. The Chrome browser will give you a cast alert in the drop down menu under the Chrome icon in the top right corner of your screen if you start casting from an optimized website.

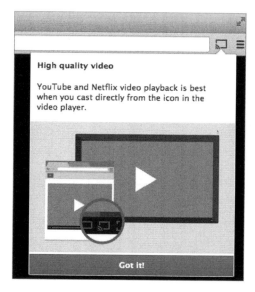

The good news is that more content providers may be optimizing their websites for Chromecast in the near future, so keep your eyes open for the Chromecast icon on their sites. Already there's a huge variety of media available for you to enjoy, and more is on the way, with many popular video and audio sites rushing to join the casting party.

That's great, but what if you want to watch stuff from all your favorite sites NOW?

TAB CASTING

Sites like ESPN, Vimeo, DailyMotion, Spotify, Flickr, ABC.com, CBS. com MLB.con, MTV.com, and many others have great video material that's not yet supported with a specific Chromecast app.

Tablet and smartphone users are out of luck if there's no app, but fortunately, the Google Cast extension in the Chrome browser lets Windows and Mac computers users "cast a tab" from the Chrome web browser.

You simply install the extension (see **Chapter 2**), open any site in a Chrome tab, and cast it.

To cast a tab, navigate in Chrome to the tab you want to cast. If you want to cast it in full screen mode, switch it to full screen in the Chrome window. Now click the Chromecast icon in the upper right corner of the toolbar. From the drop-down menu, choose the Chromecast device you want to send your cast to and give it a bit of time to load.

In a few seconds, your browser tab will start to play on your TV screen, complete with audio. Back on your computer, the Chromecast icon will change its color from gray to blue to show that the browser is tab casting. There's a mute button in the icon's drop-down menu if you need it. Click the icon again and use the drop-down menu to end the tab cast, or just close the tab in Chrome.

As of spring 2014, tab casting was still considered a beta feature. Google developed it because even its preferred content providers have been slow to optimize their sites for casting, with the exception of the four big players listed above.

More developers will be coming on board in the near future, but it's still in Google's best interest to make as much media as possible available for its little device – and we, the users, are the lucky beneficiaries.

Tab casting isn't a perfect solution. Getting video images to cast to your TV usually isn't a problem, but on some websites the audio stubbornly refuses to tag along. In particular, sites that use plug-ins such as QuickTime, Silverlight, or VLC are going to present problems when you try to cast them from Chrome.

Another audio problem in tab casting is that you can't play the sound for your tab cast through both your TV and your computer at the same time, once you start casting the audio will only play through your TV. However, you can browse in other Chrome tabs, and even play their audio through your computer speakers, while your tab cast is in progress on your TV.

If you want to tab cast in full screen mode however, you're going to need this nifty little workaround, because normally during tab casting you have to keep the video running in full screen mode on your computer to display it on your TV in full screen mode.

Simply hit Alt-Tab (in Windows) or Command-Tab (in Mac) to take your computer out of the full screen window while leaving it running on your TV. To return to the full screen window on your computer, click the untitled Chrome window in the Windows taskbar, or click the Chrome icon in the dock on your Mac.

There's also the issue of not being able to cast tabs from tablets or smartphones – the operating systems for these devices just aren't robust enough to accommodate the heavy data demands of the process. There's one bit of good news, though: the Samsung Chromebook seems to have improved to the point where it will support tab casting, even though that support isn't yet official.

MIRRORING YOUR ENTIRE DESKTOP

Occasionally you'll run across a website with video that won't play in Chrome. If you really need this video, you do have the option of opening it in another browser and mirroring your entire desktop to your TV, also called screencasting.

There are limitations to this, though – screencasting is an experimental feature, so it leaves the audio on your computer and doesn't send it to the TV speakers. It's also extremely data intensive, so you're likely to get some lags as the data buffers. And again, this function doesn't work on tablets and smartphones.

Still, it's kind of a cool feature, and one worth playing around with. With the video open on your desktop, open the Chrome browser, click the Chromecast icon in the upper right corner of the toolbar, and choose "Cast entire screen (experimental)". There are other reasons why you might want to mirror your entire screen which we will discuss later.

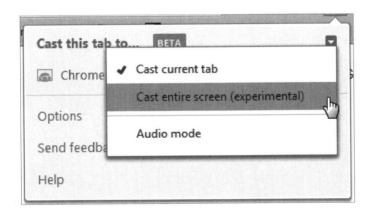

For local files stored on your computer which need to use other software programs and can't be opened easily in Chrome, mirroring your entire screen will work but there are better solutions by far. We'll look at those in **Chapter 4**.

4. PERSONALIZING YOUR CHROMECAST EXPERIENCE

In addition to the Google preferred content providers listed at the end of **Chapter 1**, there's a tremendous boom among independent developers to build Android and iOS apps for the Chromecast that do just about everything.

Google has chosen to follow its wildly successful Android business model and make the Chromecast software development kit (SDK) publicly available for free, so expect a blizzard of new apps for the device in the near future.

In this chapter, we focus on a few apps, some free and some paid, that allow you to cast your personal media collection through your Chromecast dongle. For Windows and Mac users, we touch on some workarounds to make your Chromecast do more without apps.

We also talk about the pros and cons of Plex, an app that uploads and organizes all of your media in the cloud for playback through Chromecast. Please note that we are offering this advice without any kind of compensation from the developers of the apps we recommend, so we think (or hope!) that we're being pretty objective.

CASTING LOCAL CONTENT FROM YOUR PERSONAL MEDIA COLLECTION

Many of us have "local" content – existing videos, photos and music on our computers – that we would like to cast to HDTV so we can share them on the big screen with family and friends. The problem is that some of our local content either doesn't 'live' on the web, or it's not in a format that will open and play in the Chrome browser.

That means it's not available for tab casting, and often screencasting without audio (see **Chapter 3**) really isn't a desirable option. Fortunately, there are Android and iOS apps, as well as Chrome extensions, that create a cozy relationship between your personal media and the Chromecast.

Some of them, particularly the free ones, have their limitations, in that they don't support all file formats, but you might be able to find one that works for you. So let's take a look at some of these options...

First, if you only need to cast one or two local files from your Windows or Mac computer, there's a relatively low-tech solution. You can use the Chrome browser to open files stored on your hard drive.

For Windows, simply type **file:///C:/** into the top toolbar where the website http://www. address would normally go. Mac users should type in **file://localhost/**. Hit the *Enter* key to bring up all of the folders on your hard drive.

You will probably have to click into an individual folder to find the file you're looking for. Click a file name it to open it in Chrome and then click the Chromecast icon in the top right corner of your browser window to start tab casting the file.

This process works fine for locally stored photos and music files, and you might be able to play some local videos if they're in a format that's compatible with Chrome. However, using Chrome to access your hard drive will only open one file at a time, so if you want to play a lot of media at once, it's annoyingly cumbersome.

There are other free alternatives for Windows and Mac users who want to cast a lot of local content at once.

For photos, you can upload them to an image sharing site such as **Flickr** and tab cast your personal gallery from Chrome. There are also other photo apps available, which we will look at later.

Music Manager: For music, there's the Music Manager desktop app that allows you to upload up to 20,000 songs to your personal Google Play account and play them from your Windows or Mac computer, or from your Android device. First, download Music Manager from this page – https://support.google.com/googleplay/answer/1229970

You will need to register an account and provide Google Wallet with your name and a credit card number even though the service is free.

Once you're set up, you can upload your music library to Google Play and use the Music Manager desktop app to create playlists and cast them through your computer or Android device.

> ## Hint, hint –
> this app is tailor made for migrating your iTunes library off your hard drive and into the cloud.

Videostream: For videos, there's a Chrome extension from the Chrome Web Store called **Videostream** that lets you cast your local videos directly from your computer's hard drive, instead of bothering with tab casting or screencasting.

The developer has written versions of this app for both Windows and Mac. The extension supports 25 different video formats, so you don't have to worry about trying to open a video file with an obscure file format in Chrome. It also does away with the compatibility issues that Chrome has with Silverlight, QuickTime, and VLC plug-ins.

Videostream also makes apps for Android and iOS devices that not only cast your local videos, but download video files from the internet. Before Videostream, Windows and Mac users were limited to using Plex to cast local video content if they couldn't get Chrome or screencasting to work with their video. This is a sophisticated app with some development money behind it, so it's definitely one to watch.

Avia: if you have an **Android phone or tablet**, including the Kindle Fire, you may already be familiar with this app, which organizes your entire media collection into categories and lets you sort it with graphical icons.

When the Chromecast was released, the developers got right on the job so the dongle and Avia would work hand in hand to cast directly to your HDTV. The app's support for Chromecast is an in-app paid purchase through Avia's free Android app, but the price for the upgrade is a reasonable $2.99 one-time fee.

Your first step is to install the free Avia app from the **Google Play app store for Android**, or from **Amazon's Android app store**. Once it's installed, simply pay the fee to unlock the Chromecast support feature. You'll see your Chromecast automatically listed in the device menu if you've already set it up properly (see **Chapter 2**).

Although Avia doesn't support Windows PC or Mac for Chromecast, it does support **Dropbox**, which means you can grab local media from your computer and transfer it to your Android device for casting through your phone or tablet without going through tab casting in Chrome. To do this you will need to download, install and set up

Dropbox on both your desktop computer and your mobile phone or tablet device.

The sorting of features in Avia is very nice if you have a lot of media files. Another thing to consider is that Avia will access your Plex Media Server account (see later in this chapter for the complete scoop on Plex).

Allcast: This is an Android app that works in similar fashion to Avia. Although it's not available for computers, it provides access to Dropbox and Google Drive so you can transfer your files from your PC or Mac over to your phone and use Avia to play them through Chromecast.

The free version of Allcast limits you to only one minute of video streaming; to do more, you need to upgrade to the premium version for $4.99 from the Android app store.

For some unknown reason, Google disabled Chromecast access to Allcast (previously known as Aircast) shortly after it released the device in mid-2013, but it then re-enabled access at the same time it released the Chromecast SDK, so apparently the developers are back on Google's good guy list. They are said to be working on a PC version of the app, which will open up further possibilities for the Chromecast without going through tab casting in the Chrome browser.

PLEX – ACCESS ALL YOUR MEDIA AND PLAY IT VIA CHROMECAST!

All the options listed so far in this chapters have their limitations, they will be helpful to some, but not to others. If you're looking for a "one-size fits all" solution to grabbing your media (films/music/photos) from wherever you store it and playing it on your HDTV through your Chromecast, or indeed playing it on any other device, then take a look at Plex.

Plex is another way to cast your locally stored media content to your TV, but that's only a small part of what it does. Fans of Plex (and there are many) use it because it lets them transfer all of their digital media to a single media server in the cloud and use any type of device to organize and view it.

You can easily switch back and forth between devices because they're all accessing the same stored digital files on the Plex Media Server. Wherever you are in the world you'll always have access to your content via their server. It also saves you the headache of downloading and then later deleting locally stored video to your tablet or smartphone to free up storage space.

Plex is a hot item in the tech world, and the developers have released apps for just about every device out there, including Roku and Smart TV. For our purposes, you should know that Plex apps are available for Windows and Mac, along with apps for Android and iOS.

The desktop computer apps are free. The mobile apps can be purchased for under $5 in the Google Play or iTunes store, so you don't need to subscribe to the monthly "Plex Pass" premium plan to use Plex on your smartphone or tablet.

In the dog-eat-dog world of software development, the Plex people found themselves on the receiving end of some scathing criticism on social media sites because they only offered Chromecast support to their Plex Pass paying customers.

In mid-March 2014, the company righted the ship and made Chromecast support free for all of their customers, including Android, iOS, and Windows and Mac web app users. This is fantastic news for Chromecast users and a great move by the Plex team.

Like that really smart kid you remember from school, Plex can be a bit intimidating, but don't be put off. You're not going to lose any data if you use it, so why not give it a whirl? We did, and we're hooked.

It's best to start with one simple uploading task, which for us was getting our iTunes library uploaded from our Mac laptop so we could play our songs through our Chromecast. Windows users will find the process is almost identical, and we've noted below where it's different.

Your first step is to go to the device where the local content you want to upload to Plex is stored. For us, that was our MacBook Pro. Use your web browser to navigate to the https://plex.tv home page.

Click the **Sign Up** button at the top right and register your information. You'll get an email asking you to click a link to confirm your registration. Be sure to record your user name and password for future reference.

Click the **Launch** button in the top right corner to go to the download page and install the Plex app for your computer.

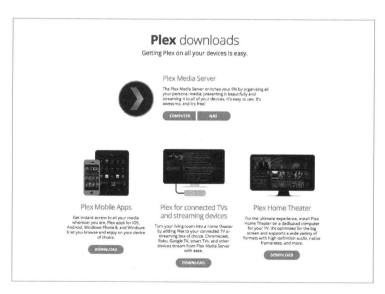

Note that you can also download an app for your tablet or smartphone from this page if that's where your local media is stored, but we downloaded the app for Mac OS. It's a big .zip file that goes to your Downloads folder.

When downloading is complete, click it open and drag the app to your Applications folder. (Windows users will put it in Programs.)

The next part is not exactly intuitive, but we just kept following the prompts and it turned out great. You need to add at least one library to your Plex account so there's a place on their storage drives to hold your media files.

Click the *Add Library* button. The app will ask you to choose a type of media from a set of graphic icons.

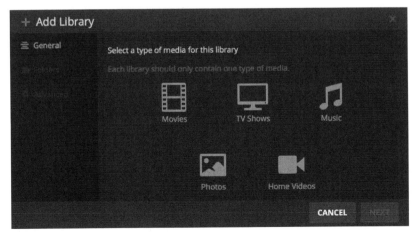

We chose Music for our iTunes library. Now Plex will want to you to show it the folder where you keep the media you want to upload. This is fairly easy on both a Mac and Windows computer since both operating systems have clearly labeled folders for music, videos, and photos.

We selected the Music folder on our Mac and then chose the iTunes library. Whoosh, suddenly our entire music collection was uploading to Plex. Success!

Now to cast...open a tab in your Chrome browser and go to https://plex.tv/web.

Log in and look for the casting icons along the top right and select your Chromecast.

Then it's just a case of selecting any of the files you've previously uploaded to start casting them to your HDTV. When you're done you can go back to the casting icon and choose *Disconnect* to stop casting.

As previously mentioned, Plex will also upload and play videos and photos though your Chromecast, plus it's a great place to store any content you value and don't want to lose.

Mac users can automate the process one step further with the **$28 Hazel software** (www.noodlesoft.com), which quietly sorts and files everything on your hard drive, including uploading your media files to Plex while you sleep.

Remember that video files aren't small, and it's a lot more fun watching a movie than watching the progress bar inch slowly to the right of your screen while you're waiting for the file to finish downloading. For mac users we'd say this add-on is excellent value for money!

5. CHROMECAST ON THE MOVE

At a size that's barely bigger than a flash drive, the Chromecast dongle is small enough to travel well. In this chapter, we look at some of the ways it can work for you outside of your home, in business, and with friends.

THE BUSINESS END OF CHROMECAST

The digital slide projector is a cumbersome piece of old school technology that seemingly has hung on forever. Now the Chromecast presents it with a credible threat, at a fraction of its weight and cost. If you give a lot of business presentations, you can expect to see it start turning up in the near future, and if you're really bold, you might want to be the first in your business network to show it off. New tech toys are a great icebreaker!

There are a couple of different ways to approach business presentations with Chromecast. If your material isn't available through an Android or iOS app for Chromecast (see **Chapter 1**), then your best bet is to tab cast directly from the Internet in the Chrome browser on your Windows or Mac computer.

You can either use existing media in the YouTube library or on the web, or you can create a presentation on Google Drive and cast that in a Chrome browser tab. It's also possible to create a Powerpoint presentation on your computer's hard drive and use the screencasting function (mirroring your entire screen) to cast it to an HDTV (this will only work for presentations with no audio track).

In any case, make sure in advance that the display device has an HDMI port, and it would be a good idea to give it a dress rehearsal before the day of your presentation.

Another issue to address in advance is password access to the wireless network that will carry your presentation. In your own office, this won't be a problem, but some networks in hotels and conference centers have very few options when it comes to joining wirelessly (see our take on this issue later in this chapter).

SOCIAL BUZZ

As well as business conferencing, the Chromecast is a great tool for sharing photos and videos when you go to visit friends and family. You might want to check in advance to make sure their TV has an HDMI port, and that they know their wireless network password.

Photowall for Chromecast is a smartphone app that is available for both Android and iOS; in fact, the beta version was first released for iOS, which caused a bit of a buzz in the tech world considering that Google tends to stay on the Android side of the fence.

Photowall not only lets you cast photos from your smartphone to HDTV, but it lets anyone sharing your Wi-Fi network do the same. There's a nifty doodle and annotation tool so you can edit your photos and add speech balloons and other personal touches. One really ingenious feature of Photowall is that it automatically generates a YouTube video montage of your photos and posts it on demand.

The Photowall app uses Google Drive to store the photos, so anyone who participates will need a Google account. PC and Mac users can access Photowall through Chrome and use tab casting to share their photos. The smartphone and tablet apps provides some great instant gratification, where you can take a photo with your phone and have it posted and shared with others on your Wi-Fi network literally within seconds – great for birthday parties, baby pictures, and pet tricks!

VIDEO CONFERENCING

Google Hangouts are a free, effective way to bring a lot of people together for a conversation, whether serious or not-so-serious. They're also way too much fun to cram into a small screen. With Chromecast it's easy to display them on your big-screen TV, and you don't need any add-on software to do it from your Windows or Mac computer. Your Chrome browser is already set up to handle the job; you just need to do a couple of things differently.

First, since Hangouts appear in a new pop-up window with no toolbar, you need to move the Hangout to a Chrome window with a toolbar. Go to the top of the hangout window, click in the box where the https://plus.google.com/ hangout address is displayed, and copy it. Open a new tab in your Chrome browser, paste in the hangout URL that you just copied, close the old pop-up window with no toolbar, and click reload in the new window with the toolbar. You now have all of your app buttons above your hangout. From here it's an easy task to tab cast the hangout just as you would any other Internet page.

One major caution: if you leave the sound turned up high on your HDTV, the microphone on your computer will pick it up and create an excruciating feedback loop. Turn the sound down low on your TV to minimize this problem.

ON THE ROAD

Believe it or not, you can even use Chromecast in your car! **This video** (http://youtu.be/DV7pzl-ZTxg) shows how to convert the dongle's HDMI signal into the RCA input that powers the built-in dashboard TV in Mercedes and other high-end vehicles. Obviously this isn't a good idea while you're driving, unless you're just streaming music, or listening to the audio on music videos. But it sure is cool!

This system wouldn't work without a tethering app. A great deal of mystery surrounds these tethering apps, which create a wireless hotspot within your vehicle (or anywhere else), giving the Chromecast a Wi-Fi signal so it can do its thing. These apps are available for both iPhone and Android if you know where to look, you can start by searching for tethering apps in the Google Play store.

Since they're third-party apps, you would need to "jailbreak" your phone to install one. Despite the sinister name, there's nothing illegal about jailbreaking a phone; it just takes some time and tech savvy.

And the FCC has ruled that cell phone providers can't ban you from adding a tethering app to your phone – however, they are free to charge you extra for your data plan if you install one! For this reason, we suspect that casting in your vehicle is mostly a novelty item – and indeed it's novel!

HOTEL ROOM ACCESS

As soon as we heard about the Chromecast, we were already having visions of taking it on trips and using it in a hotel room. All the pieces are in place: digital TV, wireless network, comfortable beds, and the need to relax with a movie at the end of a long day. All that's needed is a smartphone and the Chromecast dongle, right?

Um, not so fast. Hotel Wi-Fi networks are usually locked down so that no two devices on the network can communicate with each other. Since Chromecast requires the dongle and your casting device to hold hands, it's pretty rare to be able to use it over a hotel network without some fancy dancing. The irony is that the hotels probably don't care about steering you into their own pay-per-view TV services, which aren't a big money maker for them. The lockdown is simply a digital security measure.

There are a few workarounds however. A tethering app, the same one that works in a car, would do the job if you don't mind the hassle of installing it on your phone and your data plan doesn't take you to the cleaners for running it. A Windows PC laptop can be used as a router, but nobody seems to be having any success with Mac Internet sharing. Another option, probably the best one, is to bring your own inexpensive "travel router" on the road with you. These are available on Amazon for around $20, although they won't work in all hotels.

With any luck, as the Chromecast comes into wider use, hotels will welcome it as much as they welcome their guests and make room for it on their wireless networks.

6. MORE APPS TO CAST YOUR CHROMECAST NET A LITTLE WIDER

If you like the apps you've seen so far in this book, keep in mind that there are more on the way. Google seems determined to crowdsource the app development process so the Chromecast can dominate the digital media player market before the set-top box manufacturers know what hit them. For you, the end user, that means low prices, lots of freebies, and endless variety.

Here is a list of some of our favorite smartphone and tablet apps for use with the Chromecast. At this point in the app development life-cycle of the Chromecast, most of what's out there is going to be Android-based because that's fastest and easiest for developers to write code for and get a release out. Look for iOS and web-based versions in the near future.

Remote Apps: Never lose or fight over the remote again! The Google Play store offers several apps for Android that allows your phone to replace the remote that came with your HDTV. The basic commands are the same as your remote, including volume control, play / pause, fast forward, rewind, and seek, plus there are several Chromecast-specific commands, including ones to launch your cast, and to open apps with a double tap. Check the specs for each individual app, along with the price. Two examples are **RemoteCast**, which is free but still in beta (experimental) release, and **SmartRemote**, which is $4.99.

Collaborative Apps: Meetings are a fact of life in business, and teleconferencing is rapidly taking the place of face to face collaboration. Remote access to workplace computers and the company intranet is a must for any business that's trying to integrate teleconferencing into its operations.

The developers of the **Teamviewer** app want to help you to take your office with you wherever you go, with support for teleconferencing, server administration, and your office desktop, including all applications and documents. These functions allow users to give Powerpoint and video presentations from home or a remote location using material stored on a computer at company headquarters.

There seems to be some serious funding behind Teamviewer, as it was released in versions for Android, iPhone, iPod touch, iPad, Windows 8 (including the RT version for mobile), and Windows Phone 8. The app is free for personal use by you and your family and friends, with a paid version for businesses.

Emulation Apps: Expect more apps on the way that free you from your living room and enable screens other than your HDTV to emulate Chromecast. For example, **CheapCast** (free, still in beta release) is an Android app that allows any Android tablet or phone to receive the Chromecast signal and serve as the display.

This app currently only works for media sites like YouTube and Google Music that don't protect their content from unauthorized use with digital rights management (DRM). You'll have to wait to use it with Netflix and Google Play Movies until the developer of CheapCast has enough resources to make a deal with these content providers.

Multiple Device Apps: Many of the apps in the Android App Store support casting to other devices along with Chromecast, including gaming boxes (like Xbox or Playstation), Digital Living Network Alliance (DLNA) televisions and other Universal Plug and Play (UPnP) devices, and even Hi-Fi audio gear.

An example of this type of app is **Bubble UPnP**, an Android app with an impressive list of supported devices – not to mention a really cool name! The app is free for up to 20 minutes of streaming, while the upgrade for unlimited usage is $4.69 to unlock.

Web Streaming Apps for mobiles and tablets: These apps carry the versatility of web-based casting over to the Android world, which is great if you want to cast from your Android phone or tablet. For example, the **PlayTo Chromecast** Android app lets you cast photos, music and videos from over 150 websites, plus local media from your phone or other media servers to your Chromecast.

Gamecasting Apps: It didn't take long for the game developers to get in on the act with Chromecast. While current offerings are limited, this category of apps is going to explode in the upcoming months with more and more games that you can play on your phone or tablet and then mirror on your HDTV via your Chromecast.

One early adopter of gamecasting is **Doodlecast**, a drawing game where each player picks out a secret word, draws it on their Android phone or tablet, and lets the other players try to guess the word. No matter what level of artistic talent you have, Doodlecast drawings look surprisingly impressive on an HDTV screen.

GR8CTZ, which stands for Great Cities of the World, is a geography guessing game that takes Google Street View data from 40 cities, displays it on your Android device, and casts it to HDTV. Up to four players use the landmarks in Street View to guess which city one another is standing in. It's educational as well as fun!

Other promising games to check out in the Google Play Android App Store include the interestingly-named **Dehumanize Your Friends**, which proudly announces that it features numerous naughty words; as well as **Mystic 8 Ball**, which reliably answers your burning questions about life such as, "Does he really love me?" and, "Will the sun shine tomorrow morning?" Finally, there are the old standbys like **Hangman**, **Pirate Dice**, and the ever-reliable **Tic-Tac-Toe**.

Photocasting Apps: Android photo apps for Chromecast are a natural choice for developers, as the code isn't too complex, and every smartphone user has hundreds of photos stored and waiting to be cast in large, high-quality display format.

The **Dayframe** app has gotten some good reviews and the basic features are free, with an in-app upgrade for advanced features. **Photocast for Chromecast** has many features similar to Google's own Photowall, except that it doesn't require you to register for a Google Drive account.

Drawing Apps: Brand new to the market (April 2014) is the **CastPad for Chromecast** app. This nifty little app lets you doodle and draw straight onto your HDTV via your Android tablet or smartphone. The basic free app has just five colors to choose from and is ad supported, but you can upgrade, via an in-app purchase to unlock limitless colors and lose the ads.

App Shopping Apps: An app for downloading more apps? Sure, why not? At the moment, the search function in the Google Play Android App Store isn't very specific for tagging Chromecast apps, so you're bound to miss some good ones. The Cast Store for Chromecast app gives you an overview of all Chromecast-compatible apps in the Android App Store.

7. MORE CHROMECAST TIPS AND TRICKS

CASTING FROM YOUR KINDLE FIRE TABLET

The question was bound to come up: can you use Chromecast to cast from your Kindle Fire HD? Although Amazon hasn't willingly played the role of matchmaker between its enormous content library and the Chromecast, there are ways to cast from your Kindle Fire to your HDTV with Chromecast.

The trick is to download the Chromecast app for Android and install it on your Kindle. The following step by step guide to getting Chromecast set up on your Kindle Fire might seem daunting at first but really it isn't. Just take your time and it will be done before you know it!

Please note: this app does not support Amazon streaming video, so if that's your only goal in enabling casting from your Kindle Fire, **you don't need to install this app**. Instead take a look at our advice for Casting Amazon Instant Video below.

Before you do anything, we suggest that you download and install an Android security app from the Amazon Kindle Store. This step isn't essential, but just makes sense generally to ensure your Kindle is protected from viruses, malware and other unwanted threats. To do this, tap *Apps* in your top toolbar. Tap *Store*, tap the search icon, and type in Android security. Choose an app, download it, and install it.

Next, go back to the app store, find the **ES File Explorer** app, download and install it too.

Next, you'll need to enable "sideloading" in your Kindle, which allows you to install Android apps that aren't available in the Amazon App Store. Swipe down on your Home screen to display the Quick Settings Menu and tap *Settings*, then tap *Applications*. Go to Apps from Unknown Sources and tap *On*.

Now it's time to install Chromecast for Android...

Unfortunately this isn't an App that you can download directly to your Kindle from the Google Play App store.

Instead, you need to download the **1mobilemarket app** through the Kindle's Silk browser, so go to http://market.1mobile.com via your browser and download their app for tablets.

Now open the ES File Explorer app. This app will show you all the folders and files on your Kindle and you should now use it to locate the 1mobilemarket app which should be in your downloads folder.

Tap the icon for the 1mobilemarket app to install.

After installation is complete, open up this app and use it to search and find the Chromecast app for Android.

Download and install it, if the app doesn't install and appear straight away use the ES File Explorer app again to find it on your Kindle and install that way.

Open the Chromecast app and tap the Chromecast icon to start casting from your Kindle Fire. There you go, you're done!

The 1mobilemarket app puts some annoying ads in your Kindle notifications area from time to time, but they're not too intrusive, and really, it's worth it to make so many more apps from Google Play for Android available for your Kindle. If you decide you don't want the 1mobilemarket app on your device once you've set up the Chromecast app then feel free to delete it.

CASTING AMAZON INSTANT VIDEO

Unfortunately, the Chromecast app that you installed in the previous step does not support Amazon streaming video, including the 40,000 free movies in the Prime Instant Video library. There are plenty of other reasons to use your Kindle for casting, but Prime Instant Video is probably the biggest attraction for most people, and it's not very likely that it will be available anytime soon since it's Amazon's gold mine.

The good news is you can, instead, use video streaming on your PC or Mac to cast Prime Instant Video with Chrome tab casting as long as you disable Silverlight in your Amazon account preferences first...

Sign in to your Amazon home screen and click the small black triangle next to your name in the top right toolbar. From the **Your Account** drop-down menu, click *Your Prime Instant Video* and then click *Settings* on the toolbar at the top right. You'll need to sign in again with your email and password; then scroll down to Web Player Preferences and choose Adobe Flash Player. In this mode, casting an Amazon Instant Video is a simple matter of playing it in the Chrome browser and casting the tab.

AUDIO STREAMING FROM ITUNES AND OTHER UNSUPPORTED MEDIA

Locally stored media libraries on your PC or Mac, like iTunes, VLC, and Spotify, aren't supported in Chromecast, and full-screen casting is no help since it can't cast audio.

Of course you can always upload your local audio library to Music Manager or Plex and cast from there, but if you don't want to wait while you upload a bunch of files, there's a super simple solution in the **Chrome Remote Desktop** extension.

It's available in the **Chrome Web Store.** Go to the store, search for Remote Desktop, and click the + *Free* button to install it in your Chrome browser.

The idea is to use your computer display as a tab within this app and then use tab casting to mirror the audio through Chromecast. To make it happen, open up Chrome and click the *Customize* icon in the far upper right corner, then click *Tools* and then *Extensions*.

Configure the Remote Desktop extension by checking the Enabled box and also the box next to Allow Access to File URLs. Grant the necessary permissions, start the app, and cast it as a tab. You'll be able to hear your audio files through the sound system on your HDTV.

SPLIT VIDEO AND AUDIO INTO SEPARATE ENTERTAINMENT EQUIPMENT

Hard core audiophiles won't be much impressed with the audio from the Chromecast's HDMI port played back through a conventional HDTV. However, it can be improved with the addition of an HDMI audio extractor, which funnels the video and audio signals from the HDMI into separate equipment.

This inexpensive piece of equipment can go a long way toward bringing your Chromecast audio up to snuff without investing in an expensive A/V receiver. Go to a site like Amazon and search for "HDMI audio extractors" to see some of the options available.

ADD EMOJI TO YOUR CHROMECAST DEVICE NAME

If you're a fan of Japanese ideograms, you're probably already familiar with the Emoji Android and iOS apps. The Chromecast app can run Emoji as an add-on, so instead of giving your Chromecast device a boring text name like "Bedroom TV" you can create an Emoji name and matching icons for it.

Emoji also works for Chromecast in the Mac OS X Chromecast app, as well as the Chromecast app for Windows 8.

IF YOU REALLY KNOW WHAT YOU'RE DOING...

If you're one of those people who just has to tinker around under the hood, you'll want to take a look at Chromecast's hidden settings. From your Windows PC or Mac, click on the Chromecast icon in the top right corner of your Chrome browser and click Options from the drop-down menu.

If you right-click anywhere within the Options menu and select Inspect Element, you'll get a pop-up window with several streaming settings that you might be familiar with from other video software.

They include items like bit rate and frame rate. There's also a Custom Mirroring Settings menu, which we recommend that you don't change until there's more documentation available for it.

Google Cast extension options

Custom mirroring settings

Changing these may have unintended consequences. Be careful.

Video Settings

Minimum bitrate:	kbps (min)
Maximum bitrate:	kbps (max)
Max quantization:	
Video buffer:	ms
Maximum tab frame rate:	fps
Resolution:	

Audio Settings

Audio bitrate:	kbps (-)

Network Settings

Pacing:	Enable pacing (M28 or later)
TCP:	Enable audio TCP Enable video TCP
NACK:	Enable Audio NACK

Right now the Chromecast is so new that we suspect the hidden settings are placeholders, because we've found that changing them doesn't seem to have any effect. Nonetheless, we thought we'd let you know they exist, in case the next update to Chromecast makes them operable.

RESTORING YOUR CHROMECAST SETTINGS TO FACTORY DEFAULTS

There are two common instances where you might want to reset the Chromecast dongle to factory default settings. The first is if you sell it or give it away, and the second is if you replace your wireless network and set up one with new specs.

In either case, if you don't reset it the Chromecast will patiently continue to hunt for the network you were using when you went through the setup process.

To restore factory defaults, find the small button on the round edge of the device at the larger end, opposite the HDMI plug. With the device unplugged from your TV but plugged in through its USB cable, press and hold this button for at least 30 seconds.

Let the indicator light go from blinking white to red and back to white again. When the reset is finished, you or the new owner will need to go through the setup process all over again, just as if the device were new out of the box.

8. LOOKING DOWN THE PIPELINE

As we were researching this book, we were continually amazed at the possibilities for innovation contained in the Chromecast, a $35 package measuring less than three inches long. The early days of a ground-breaking tech product are always exciting because there are so many independent software developers trying to get in on the ground floor. The creativity of so many smart people working on their own projects is astonishing.

This is the power of crowdsourcing, and when it comes to crowdsourcing, nobody does it better than Google. After initially launching the Chromecast with only a few dedicated apps from large media companies, Google seems to have made a conscious effort to open up the field and model the device after its wildly successful Android app program. Currently the Android App Store contains over 750,000 titles, many of them free. What better way to get everyone using your device than to give away the software to run it?

With that in mind, Google announced in February 2014 that they would be releasing the Chromecast SDK (software developer kit) and selling it for a mere $5.00. This will allow app developers to easily add Chromecast support to their existing apps, as well as build brand new ones especially for the Chromecast.

Google claims that the SDK is so simple that it contains less than 200 lines of code, making it possible for beginning developers to write an app for Chromecast.

As you play with the various features on your Chromecast, you've probably already figured out that Google developed tab casting from a computer as a stop-gap measure. The idea is to get as many customers on board as early as possible and build demand for the device while developers get busy building apps and optimizing their websites for casting from a desktop.

The Chromecast landscape is going to look a lot busier – and better – in only a year from now. And in five years? We think the sky is the limit!

ANOTHER QUICK REMINDER ABOUT UPDATES

As we mentioned at the start of the book, the Chromecast, and indeed all media streaming services, like Apple TV, Roku and the brand new Amazon Fire TV, are still in their infancy. The landscape is changing all the time with new services, apps and media suppliers appearing daily.

Staying on top of new developments is our job and if you sign up to our free monthly newsletter we will keep you abreast of news, tip and tricks for all your streaming media equipment.

If you want to take advantage of this, sign up for the updates HERE…

http://lyntons.com/chromecast-updates

Don't worry; we hate spam as much as you do so we will never share your details with anyone.

Made in the USA
San Bernardino, CA
18 December 2014